My name's Nancy McNutty, trainee reporter.
I was just a peanut butter sandwich trying
to get my big break in a tough world.

But it wasn't proving easy.
Especially with a boss like Big Cheese.

But then the phone rang. It was Marvin, my sauce at Lemon Labs.

The situation sounded serious so I knew I had to get to Lemon Labs — FAST!

I needed to catch up with the monster but there was already panic amongst the citizens. So, I hitched a lift through the crowd.

The fire service tried to control it.

I'd seen enough destruction and knew this had to stop. But how?
I was just a peanut butter sandwich – what could I do?
Maybe the Doughnut had a weakness. It was time to talk to Professor Nutcase.

That's when I knew it was time to stop reporting the action and be a part of it.

And then . . . everything went black.

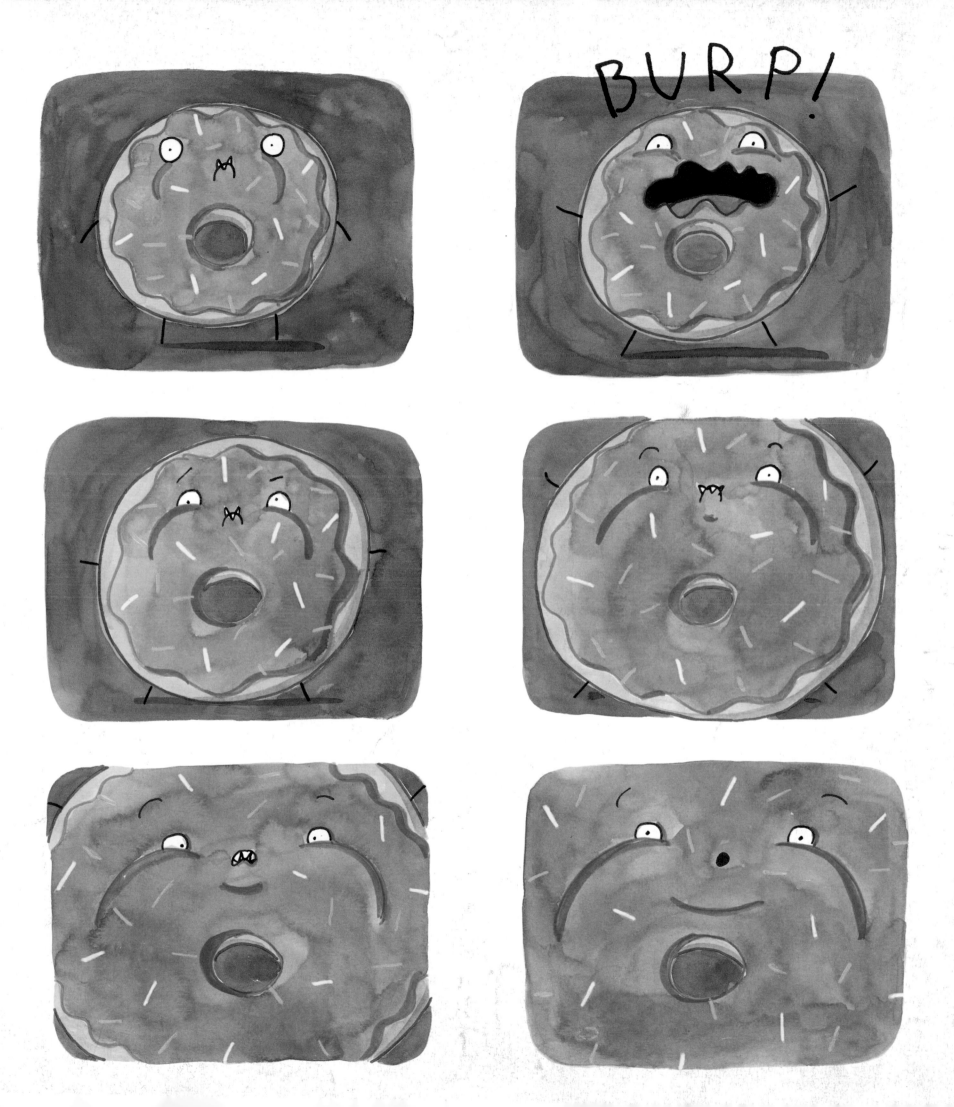

That day, instead of writing the news, I **was** the news.
Once again, Food Town was safe . . .